Let's Have Some Music

Game Songs for Children

Music by Darius Milhaud
English text by Jeremy Drake

DURAND

La version originale est éditée chez Durand (© 1933).
Les paroles d'origine sont d'Armand Lunel.

///

DF 15644

Performance Notes

— The mischievous students are placed on the left; the obedient students on the right.

— A student from the group involved announces each upcoming song.

— The performance can be accompanied by a corresponding pantomime, if desired.

— Individual movements may be performed separately.

— An easy orchestral accompaniment (violins and cellos) is available. The parts are sold separately.

Duration: 14 minutes

Index

to Mrs. Elizabeth Spague Coolidge

LET'S HAVE SOME MUSIC

Game Songs for Children

English text by
Jeremy Drake

music by
Darius Milhaud

1. A Little Test

Dialogue, by obedient students

D & F 15644

What a hope-less dunce you are! O-sa-ka is in Ja-pan. Thes-sa-ly is part of Greece.

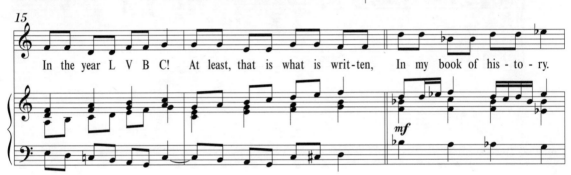

Is Pe-king in Pa-ki-stan? Where are Dun-bar and Dum-fries? Cae-sar came to vis-it Brit-ain,

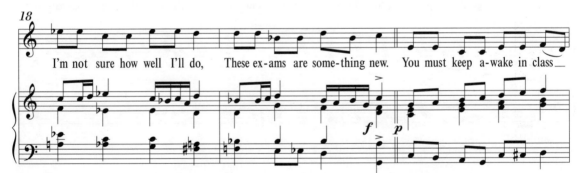

In the year L V B C! At least, that is what is writ-ten, In my book of his-to-ry.

I'm not sure how well I'll do, These ex-ams are some-thing new. You must keep a-wake in class

Oth-er-wise you might not pass!

2. Skipping Song

Dialogue, by mischievous students

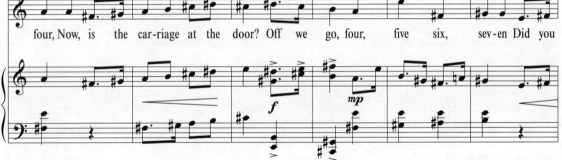

cross the Me - nai Strait? Off we go, six, sev - en eight nine Sail - ing

down the riv - er Tyne. Off we go, sev - en eight, nine, ten. To a

pret - ty Scot - tish glen._____ Is there room for

me in - side? Hur - ry up! Where is the guide? On your bike, or

in your car, You'll be go-ing ver-y far. If a train will

suit you fine, You'll be rush-ing down the line. Do you want to

take a plane Just to go to Am-ster-dam? I think you are

quite in - sane, You could get there in a train!

3. Reading Lesson

Spelling Song, by obedient students

Zo - e, your ze - bra Zonks in al - ge - bra,

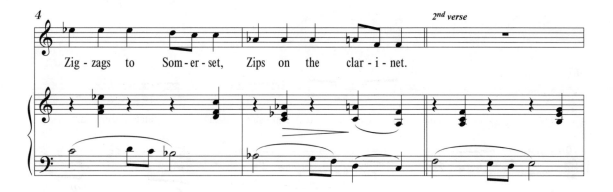

Zig - zags to Som - er - set, Zips on the clar - i - net.

A zeal - ous Zu - lu In Hon - o - lu - lu, Rides on a zith - er,

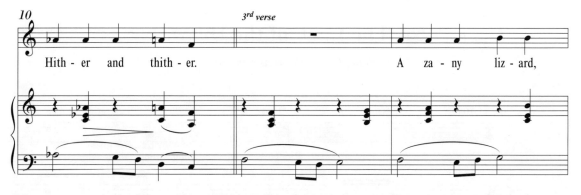

4. The Luck of the Draw

Song, by mischievous students

Plong! Ding dong ding dong ding

click! What was that? It was a stick. Since when do sticks go click? O - ho! You're a

dunce and out you go! Plong! A chick-en crossed the

road. Did it walk or did it fly? It was car-ried by a toad. Out you

5. Miss Spectacles

Round, by mischievous students

Vif
1st verse

Miss Spec - ta - cles is wor - ried Since

she got out of bed. ____ She's flus - tered and she's flur - ried, For

she has lost her head! What the dick - ens will hap - pen? She

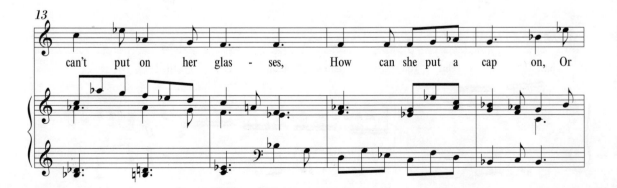

can't put on her glas - ses, How can she put a cap on, Or

37 Rondo

42

47

52

57

62

cried

Then at last she can   see it, Still   fast a-sleep in   bed!

6. Mea Culpa

Song, by obedient students

14

7. The Monitor Alexander

Round, by mischievous students

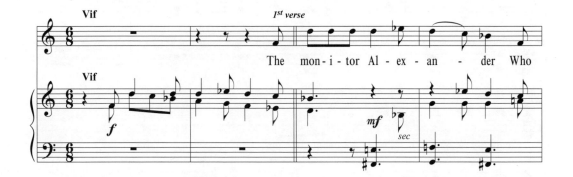

The mon-i-tor Al-ex-an — der Who

should be our com-man — der In fact has not a clue. If there's an-y-one

fight — ing Or an-y-thing___ ex-cit — ing, Oh dear, what can he

do? He'll stamp and storm and tear his hair, But we just real-ly

8. Deserved Praise

Song, by obedient students

-ten-tion and do-ing our best, We're nev - er gig - gling, nev - er smirk-ing.

And we keep ver - y clean, we're im-pec-ca-bly dressed, We're ver - y

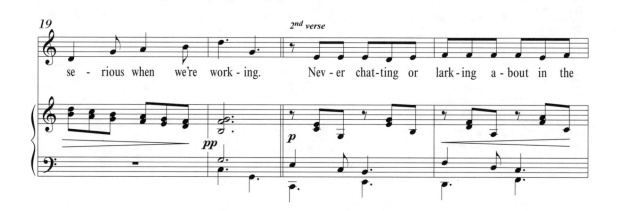

se - rious when we're work-ing. Nev - er chat-ting or lark-ing a-bout in the

class We fin - ish all our ex - er - cis - es. Ev - er reach-ing a

lev - el we want to sur - pass, That's how we win so man - y priz - es.

La - ter on if we have our own kids we shall say: If you can

do as well as we did, It's a - gree - a - ble go - ing to school ev - 'ry

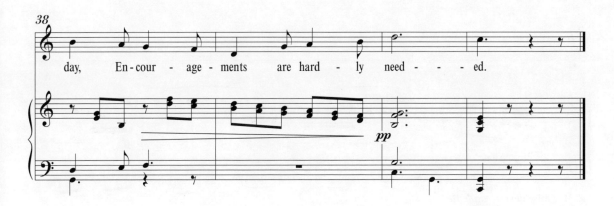

day, En - cour - age - ments are hard - ly need - - - ed.

20

9. The Argument

Dialogue, by all students*

* *M. : mischievous students*
  O. : obedient students

21

load of lit-tle swots, Who spoil our fun and games! And you're a bunch of clots, For call-ing us those names!

We'll tear your books in two, And fill your pens with glue, What a hul - la-ba-loo!

We'll tell the teach-er all, You'll both-er us no

more, He will give you what for!

22

M.
You think you're ver-y bright, Be-cause your marks are good. You hav-en't un-der-stood, You're just a trog-lo-dyte!
O.
You'll see when you leave school, Un-worth-y par-a-site! You say that out of spite, You sil-ly, lit-tle fool!
TOGETHER
You sil-ly, lit-tle fool!
You're just a trog-lo-dyte!

10. The Orchestra of the Obedient Students

by obedient students

sound is smooth and mel - low, El - e - gant and full of

grace! These won-der - ful in - stru - ments Give to

all the great - est pleas - ure. They mer - it our

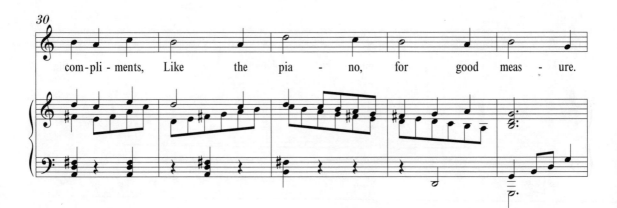

com-pli - ments, Like the pia - no, for good meas - ure.

Next, the flute and clar-i-net, The French horn and the trom-bone,

With the tu-ba and the trum-pet, Al-so have a pret-ty tone.

Ah, you on-ly have to prac-tice Then you'll en-

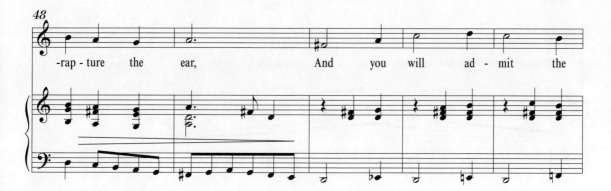

-rap-ture the ear, And you will ad-mit the

26

fact is Hard work is not so aus - tere. And

e - ven the tim-pa - ni, Or the bass drum and the

gong, Will gen - er - ate eu - pho - ny.

If you're skilled, you can't go wrong.

11. The Orchestra of the Mischievous Students

by mischievous students

28

Why should we scratch a gui - tar? It's un-plea-sant to the ear Why do they

want us to hear Sounds that we find so bi - zarre? It is

3rd verse

all too com - pli - cat - ed, With a walk - man it's much

bet - ter Both for jazz and op - er - et - ta. How much more so-phis - ti -

30

12. Final Chorus: In Praise of Computers

by all students

work, ___ Have great fun be - fore the screen,

It's a thing you've nev - er seen, _____ For it is some - thing we won't

Farandole-Galop

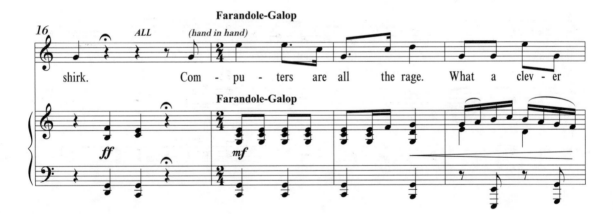

shirk. Com - pu - ters are all the rage. What a clev - er

ap - pa - rat - us! Now the e - lec - tron - ic page Is the one that

will___ e - late_____ us. Com - pu - ters are all the rage,

With them we en - joy our home-work. It's the in - for - ma - tion age,

Ev - 'ry - one is on___ a___ net - - - - work. Com - pu - ters are

all the rage, In our schools and in our hous - es, Think of all the

34

D & F 15644